# Coping with 1999 Diary

PETER COREY
illustrated by
Philip Reeve

IF THIS DIARY DARES TO ROAM, BOX ITS EARS AND SEND IT HOME TO...

NAME: ........................................

ADDRESS: ........................................

........................................

........................................

........................................

TEL NO.: ........................................

SCHOOL: ........................................

........................................

........................................

FORM NUMBER: ........................................

TEACHER'S NAME: ........................................

TEACHER'S NICKNAME: ........................................

PET(S): ........................................

BEST FRIEND(S):

(with plenty of space for changes)

........................................

........................................

........................................

........................................

BOY/GIRLFRIEND(S):

(with plenty of space for changes)

........................................

........................................

........................................

........................................

ANY OTHER DETAILS: ........................................

........................................

........................................

........................................

# COPING WITH THIS DIARY

It couldn't be simpler. Well, that's a lie for a start. It could easily be simpler. Much simpler. For a start, I could simply fill out all the entries for you so that you didn't have anything to do. But then that would hardly make it your diary, would it? So I've left most of it blank. I say "most of it" because I have provided you with sound advice, handy hints and even a few useful(-ish!) facts and other stuff to make your journey through 1999 and out of the century as painless as possible. There's even a space at the back to put some useful addresses and phone numbers. Yes! It's just like a real diary! All you have to do is remember to fill it in.

**Countdown to oblivion (sorry – millennium)**

1999 is a momentous year. Not only is it the end of the twentieth century, but it also leads to the beginning of the New Millennium! This diary will provide you with a timetable to help you get the most out of your own personal millennium celebrations.

**Dedication**

This diary is dedicated to Samuel Pepys, the famous diarist. Because of what he put in his diary, it should be read by anyone who wants a good sense of history.

This diary is not dedicated to Roger the Dog. Because of what he *did* in his diary it should be avoided by anyone with a good sense of smell.

**Note:** The school holiday dates in this diary are based on the official ones issued by the DfEE. You may find that yours are completely different – in which case – SORRY.

# DECEMBER 1998

## Monday 28

Only four days to go till the end of the year! Boy, has 1998 been a tough year or what! 1999 can't possibly be any worse – can it !?!

## Tuesday 29

Time to start making those New Year's resolutions!

## Wednesday 30

## Thursday 31

New Year's Eve

## Friday 1

New Year's Day, not surprisingly!

**New Year's Resolutions – a quick guide**

**"I'll walk the dog/keep my pet clean":** This resolution lasts months, because it's an easy one to get around. **"I'll keep my room tidy":** Shelf life of a week – assuming that you only plan to tidy it once a week. If you plan to tidy it every day then the resolution lasts a day, tops. **"I'll be nice to my little...":** This one won't even last until you get to the end of the sentence, so just don't bother!

## Saturday 2

Time to start BREAKING those New Year's resolutions!

## Sunday 3

# JANUARY

## Monday 4

New Year's holiday in Scotland.

Back to school about now! Yuck!

## Tuesday 5

## Wednesday 6

Twelfth Night: Christmas decorations need to be down by now.

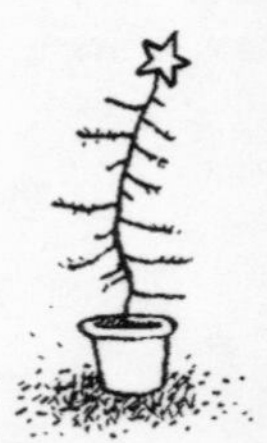

## Thursday 7

Russian Orthodox Christmas Day

If you're short on presents, head off to Russia!

## Friday 8

## Saturday 9

## Sunday 10

**January – where does it come from?**
The Roman calendar had ten months, but the Roman King, Numa Pompilious, liked them so much he added another two. He added January, named after the Roman god Janus, who symbolized new beginnings, even though January was the eleventh month in those days, not the first. Oh well, you can't expect the Romans to be good at everything! But as far as you're concerned, January probably means "mocks".

# JANUARY

## Monday 11

1569: The first State lottery was held in Britain. The slogan was probably: "It couldest be Thou!"

## Tuesday 12

## Wednesday 13

## Thursday 14

Saint Hilary's Day – supposedly the coldest day of the year.

## Friday 15

## Saturday 16

## Sunday 17

Feast Day of Saint Anthony – patron saint of pigs. A real chance to "pig out"!

**Sunday – what does it mean?**

Sunday means quite simply "The day of the Sun". Ancient civilizations worshipped the Sun long before the *Mirror* and the *Daily Mail* came along. Of course, there was no instant bingo in those days, but then there wasn't much else either, unless you count mud and wild animals.

# JANUARY

## Monday 18

Let's make this "Be nice to little brothers Week". If you haven't got a little brother, find someone else's little brother to be nice to – after all, it'll save them having to do it!

## Tuesday 19

## Wednesday 20

## Thursday 21

Aquarius starts here.

## Friday 22

## Saturday 23

Feast Day of Saint Obesolard – patron saint of pigging out on chocolate. Sorry – this is one I've made up. But don't let that stop you pigging out!

## Sunday 24

That "Be nice to little brothers" thing – it's not going to work. What about making next week "Feed little brothers to next door's cat Week"?

All Aquarians are a bit wet – as in "damp". They leave little trails of water wherever they go. So they tend to go for jobs and hobbies where their affliction won't be made too obvious, such as plumbing and swimming – often at the same time.

Aquarius – the year ahead: Lots of red faces when people say: "Did you do that on my carpet?"

# JANUARY

## Monday 25

### Burns' Night

Robert Burns was Scotland's greatest living poet, until he died in 1796, when he became Scotland's greatest dead poet. Every year on his birthday Scots people celebrate by eating lots of haggis (meat and oats mushed together in a sheep's stomach), and reciting his poetry, though not at the same time!

## Tuesday 26

## Wednesday 27

## Thursday 28

## Friday 29

## Saturday 30

## Sunday 31

Saint Bridget's Eve. Whichever direction the wind blows this evening it will blow for the rest of the year. That's assuming that you've got wind in the first place.

# SAINT VALENTINE'S DAY EXPLAINED

Valentine's Day is only a couple of weeks away – but what is it all about? Well, there were in fact two Saint Valentines, and both of them were martyred by the Romans, who were pretty keen on that sort of thing. But strangely enough, neither of them had any connection with love or snogging.

Valentine One was a bishop of Turni, about 60 miles from Rome, who was brought to Rome in about AD 273. He was beaten and then had his head chopped off. Not very romantic really!

Valentine Two was a priest and doctor who was martyred under Claudius II in AD 350. No one seems to know why.

Some scholars think that they could be the same person. In which case, the dates are wrong!

Saint Valentine's Day as we know it probably comes from the ancient belief that birds chose their mates on 14 February. The male took bits of twig to his chosen female. If she accepted the twig they became mates. Obviously he'd rather have taken flowers or chocolates – but that sort of stuff is really hard to get in your beak. Try it some time!

And all because the lady loves TWIGS™

# FEBRUARY

## Monday 1

### February – where does it come from?

This month was King Numa's second big mistake, which will become clearer as we move through the year. It's named after Februa, the Roman festival of purification. So every February people had a bath, whether they needed it or not.

New month – new start! So why not do all your homework all month!

## Tuesday 2

Candlemass. Early Christians believed that on this day "witches were abroad". In Spain probably – taking advantage of the cheap winter holiday breaks.

## Wednesday 3

## Thursday 4

## Friday 5

## Saturday 6

1969: In Rosewood near Ipswich in Queensland, it rained dead sardines. It's true! Listen, I couldn't even begin to make this stuff up!

## Sunday 7

Oh well - maybe you could try the homework thing again in March...

## FEBRUARY

### Monday 8

### Tuesday 9

### Wednesday 10

### Thursday 11

## Friday 12

## Saturday 13

Ideal Saint Valentine's Day gift for tomorrow – *Coping With Love*, a brilliant book by Peter Corey!

## Sunday 14

Saint Valentine's Day

Smile or cringe as you go through this St. V's checklist:
If you sent twigs instead of a card or chocs – oooopps!
If you signed your card – oh dear!
Ditto leaving the price on. WRONG!
If you got a card and you knew who it was from, I hope you didn't say: "This is much nicer than the one so-and-so sent me!"

# FEBRUARY

## Monday 15

Half term – probably!

## Tuesday 16

Chinese New Year – the Year of the Rabbit.
Shrove Tuesday – or Pancake Day! A day to try and stick bits of dough on to the ceiling.

## Wednesday 17

Happy New Year to Tibetans!
Ash Wednesday, when you eat up the burnt ashes of the failed pancakes.

## Thursday 18

Pisces starts here.

## Friday 19

## Saturday 20

## Sunday 21

All people who are born under the sign of the fish are a bit slippery. They also have the unfortunate habit of opening and closing their mouths, and not only when they're talking. Favourite name – "Bob", favourite food – ants' eggs.

Pisces – the year ahead: Lots of staring through glass and saying "Bob".

# FEBRUARY

## Monday 22

## Tuesday 23

Samuel Pepys' birthday.

## Wednesday 24

## Thursday 25

## Friday 26

## Saturday 27

## Sunday 28

**Countdown to Millennium:**
It's about now that you ought to start planning your Millennium celebration for 31 December. The best way to do this is to bring together a group or official committee of interested parties, i.e. a couple of friends, a brother or sister (or they'll only sulk), somebody with money who doesn't mind parting with it, and the family pet. Once your committee is formed, sit around discussing things. This will take months.

# MARCH

## Monday 1

Saint David's Day – patron saint of Wales.
Schools go back about now.

## Tuesday 2

## Wednesday 3

## Thursday 4

## Friday 5

## Saturday 6

## Sunday 7

The month of March is named after Mars – the god of war and chocolate. There's an old Roman saying: "A war a day helps you work, rest and play", and so March is traditionally the month for starting wars. Since the Romans were quite keen on wars and conquering people, throughout March the Roman army could be seen marching off to find another country to pillage.

# MARCH

## Monday 8

Commonwealth Day

**Monday – what does it mean?**

Just as Sunday was the day of Sun worship, so Monday was – yes! You've guessed it! – the day of moon worship. Anyway, the hare is the traditional animal of the moon, which is where the Mad March Hare comes from. Don't ask me where navel fluff comes from because I don't know.

## Tuesday 9

1562: A law was passed in Naples making kissing in public punishable by death! Argh!

## Wednesday 10

## Thursday 11

## Friday 12

## Saturday 13

## Sunday 14

**Mother's Day**

Buy your Mum a huge bunch of flowers that costs a FORTUNE! Mums are GREAT! (They're also famous for reading other people's diaries)

## MARCH

### Monday 15

The Ides of March – this was the day on which Julius Caesar was assassinated. Not a good day to get assassinated – he wouldn't have had chance to take his videos back after the weekend or anything.

### Tuesday 16

### Wednesday 17

Saint Patrick's Day – patron saint of Ireland.

SHAMROCK REAL ROCK BLACKPOOL ROCK

### Thursday 18

## Friday 19

## Saturday 20

The first day of spring.

## Sunday 21

Aries starts here.

Impetuous and compulsive, Arians like to get their head down. Their favourite word is "but". They like to use the top of their heads to open things: doors, windows, tins of peach slices in a light syrup. Their perfect date would be somebody with long shaggy hair who said "Baa!" a lot. Their ideal home would be on the side of a great, big mountain.

Aries – the year ahead: Lots of being frightened by dogs.

# MARCH

## Monday 22

1888: English Football League was formed.

## Tuesday 23

## Wednesday 24

## Thursday 25

## Friday 26

## Saturday 27

## Sunday 28

**Palm Sunday**

British Summer Time starts.

REMEMBER TO PUT THE CLOCKS FORWARD ONE HOUR!

In the summer there are more hours of daylight. By putting the clocks forward you increase the total hours of daylight by – yes! You worked it out! – an hour! This was originally to help farmers, especially those who were afraid of the dark. Now it's just a way of confusing the rest of the world.

# MARCH/APRIL

## Monday 29

## Tuesday 30

## Wednesday 31

## APRIL
## Thursday 1

April Fools' Day

The Jewish Passover begins.

Break up for Easter holidays – yippee!

**Friday 2**
Good Friday

**Saturday 3**

**Sunday 4**
Easter Sunday

FIND THE HIDDEN EGG - JUST FOR FUN!

## April Fools' Day explained

Under the old calendar the year began on 25 March and the New Year celebrations went on until 1 April. When New Year's Day changed to 1 January, some people just couldn't handle it. These people became known as April Fools and everyone played mean tricks on them, such as saying: "Oh look – the back of your head's on fire!" How anyone is supposed to check that beats me. Traditionally these tricks have to stop at 12 noon. After all, you can have too much fun.

# THE CHINESE NEW YEAR

## WHAT'S ALL THAT ABOUT THEN?

The Chinese calendar goes in twelve-year cycles, with each year named after a different animal. But how did this come about? According to legend, Buddha invited all the animals in his kingdom to a New Year's party. Unfortunately, only twelve turned up. And none of them brought a friend. You can probably imagine the embarrassment: tables groaning with Twiglets and only a dozen guests turn up, some of whom prefer eating each other to party nibbles.

But who were these guests? Well, there was a Rat, an Ox, a Tiger, a Rabbit, a Dragon, a Snake, a Horse, a Goat, a Monkey, a Rooster, a Dog and a Pig.

There's some confusion about the Rabbit. According to some scholars it was a cat, but I can now exclusively reveal how the confusion arose. It was in fact a cat, but when the cat – we'll call him Simon – arrived at the party he discovered that there was a house rule: No cats! Well, Simon was a real party animal so he quickly improvised a pair of huge ears out of his party invitation and went in as a rabbit. Amazingly this disguise fooled everyone, even though he had "you are cordially" printed on one ear and "smart casual" on the other.

The party went with a swing, apart from a couple of nasty incidents; the Dog kept sniffing everyone's bottom, the Tiger took a piece out of the Pig's leg and the Dragon set fire to the east wing of Buddha's palace. But everyone agreed that it was a night to remember – even the fire brigade.

So Buddha decreed that every year in a twelve year cycle should be named after one of the animal guests. And so the years became known as: Shu the Rat, Niu the Ox, Hu the Tiger, Tu the Rabbit (formerly Simon the Cat), Long the Dragon, She the Snake, Ma the Horse, Yang the Goat, Hou the Monkey, Ji the Rooster, Gou the Dog and Zhu the Pig.

There was a thirteenth guest, Derek the Tortoise, but unfortunately by the time he arrived the party had been over for three months, even though he'd travelled there by skateboard.

## APRIL

### Monday 5

Easter Monday – bank holiday in England, Wales and N. Ireland.

### Tuesday 6

### Wednesday 7

**April – where does it come from?**

The name April comes from the Roman god *Aperilus*, which comes from the word *aperire*, which comes from *Old Froggbert's Really Huge Dictionary of Stupid Words That Are Totally Impossible To Spell*. It means to open, because about this time of year the earth would open up to receive seeds for new crops. Obviously it wouldn't do this all by itself – you had to threaten it a bit with a shovel first.

## Thursday 8

## Friday 9

Saint Casilda's Day – the patron Saint of dysentery. Honestly! I'm not making it up!

## Saturday 10

## Sunday 11

# APRIL

## Monday 12

With SATS and GCSEs only a few weeks away it might be an idea to start studying. On the other hand it might not!

## Tuesday 13

Thai New Year

## Wednesday 14

New Year's Day in the state of Punjab and in Malaya.

This could be a great week for travelling around doing new year's parties. Just check that your school bus pass covers you for this sort of thing!

## Thursday 15

## Friday 16

1912: The *Titanic* was launched. They thought it was unsinkable. Ooops!

## Saturday 17

Muslim New Year

## Sunday 18

# APRIL

## Monday 19

Summer term starts about now. Yuck!

Ok – so you've had your hols. You really ought to start studying for your exams now. (If you've got some. Don't bother if you haven't!)

Swimming and School.

## Tuesday 20

Might sleep over Jessi's house.

## Wednesday 21

Taurus starts here.

French
Tennis
Daddys

Taureans are not known for their good manners. In fact, they fly into a rage the minute somebody waves a coat at them. Fortunately, this hardly ever happens. Taureans are naturally clumsy – which could be a hazard in somewhere like – say – a china shop.

Taurus – the year ahead: Lots of saying: "Are you waving your coat at me?" to people, but not in china shops hopefully.

**Thursday 22**

**Friday 23**

Saint George's Day – patron saint of England.

**Saturday 24**

**Sunday 25**

## APRIL

### Monday 26

You really ought to start studying for your exams!

### Tuesday 27

### Wednesday 28

### Thursday 29

## Friday 30

## Saturday 1 MAY

### May Day

At one time on this day on village greens the length and breadth of the British Isles people would dance around maypoles until they either got very tired or very tangled up. Then they'd crown the May Queen, who is probably based on the Roman goddess Flora, or the Greek goddess Utterly Butterly.

## Sunday 2

# HANDY STUFF FOR EXAM AND TEST TIME

By now you could actually be right in the thick of your exams. Well, hopefully not *too* thick, otherwise there won't be a lot of point in taking them. But now might be a good time to offer a bit of friendly advice to help you through. So here goes:

GET TO BED EARLY!

Going to bed some time in early May and getting up again in late July is absolute favourite.

REVISE, REVISE AND THEN REVISE!

Around about exam time parents, teachers, even complete strangers, will be full of advice about how to pass your exams. The only way to avoid this is to say, "Sorry – can't stop. I've got to revise!"

STAY FIT!

During exam time it's really important to stay fit. Running for instance. Practise running from your house to as far away as possible. This will come in really handy when you have to tell your parents your results!

DURING EXAMS. . .

You'll find that – whatever type of exam you are sitting – there will be a few important rules. Such as:

**Don't cheat!**

Unless you can be absolutely certain of getting away with it!

**Don't eat!**

Especially during swimming exams.

**Don't talk!**

Especially on the 'phone!

If you're still having problems, read my book – *Coping with Exams and Tests.*

# MAY

## Monday 3

May bank holiday

You really really really ought to start studying for your exams!

## Tuesday 4

## Wednesday 5

1821: Napoleon died.

## Thursday 6

## Friday 7

## Saturday 8

## Sunday 9

**Countdown to Millennium – update 1:**
After much discussion, argument and soul-searching, your personal Millennium Committee will probably have a list that looks like this:
1 Twiglets
2 Pop
3 Erm...
Think again! This Millennium thingy is a much bigger event!

## Monday 10

You really really really really ought to start studying for your exams!

## Tuesday 11

**Tuesday – what does it mean?**

Tuesday is the day of the Anglo-Saxon god Tiw, who was not popular on account of having a silly name. Most gods realized fairly early on that worshippers like to call out your name, so having a silly one is a real mistake. Tiw's Roman equivalent is Mars, the god of war (and chocolate as mentioned earlier), which at least doesn't sound like a sneeze.

## Wednesday 12

**Thursday 13**

**Friday 14**

**Saturday 15**

**Sunday 16**

# MAY

## Monday 17

You really really really really ought to... oh you know the score!!!

## Tuesday 18

## Wednesday 19

## Thursday 20

## Friday 21

Schools break up for half term (probably).

## Saturday 22

Gemini starts here.

All Geminis are identical twins, whether they know it or not. And to make matters worse, one is always good and the other is always bad. Which means that it never really matters how well a Gemini behaves, they'll get the blame anyway! Obviously if you are a twin AND a Gemini, then there are FOUR of you!

Gemini – the year ahead: Double trouble!

## Sunday 23

# HAVE A RELAXING HALF-TERM

Yippee! It's half term! But how are you going to relax without wearing yourself out? After all, you might be in the middle of exams, in which case the last thing you want to be doing is exerting yourself. Here are a few handy hints to having fun without having to make an effort.

PLAY RACQUET SPORTS FROM THE COMFORT OF YOUR OWN BED.

ALWAYS TAKE A COMFY CHAIR TO THE DISCO...

## MAY

### Monday 24

Summer half term (probably).

### Tuesday 25

### Wednesday 26

### Thursday 27

## Friday 28

## Saturday 29

1953: Mount Everest was climbed for the first time.

## Sunday 30

## Monday 31

Spring bank holiday all over (including Scotland this time!).

## Tuesday 1 JUNE

The Romans decided to call their fourth month Junius after Juno, the Roman goddess of the Moon, women and childbirth. From July onwards, the Romans quickly ran out of gods to call the months after, which is really amazing because they had gods for everything.

SHAVUS

GOD OF SHAVING

FEEDUS

URP

GOD OF FOOD

TOYS-R-US

GOD OF CHILD ORIENTED CONSUMER GOODS

## Wednesday 2

## Thursday 3

## Friday 4

## Saturday 5

Britain made its first space flight.

## Sunday 6

# JUNE

## Monday 7

## Tuesday 8

## Wednesday 9

## Thursday 10

## Friday 11

## Saturday 12

## Sunday 13

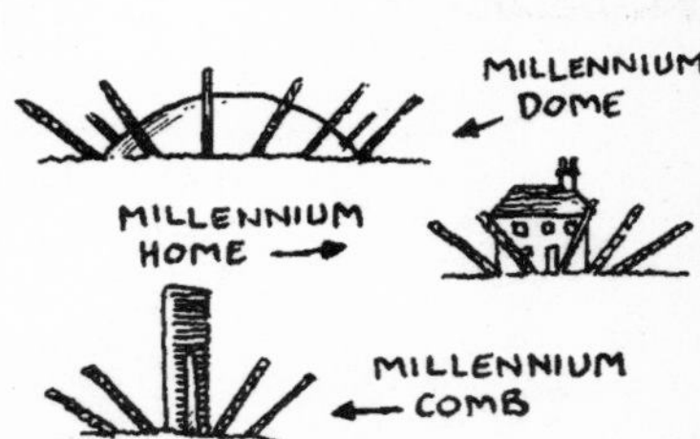


**Countdown to Millennium – update 2:**
By now your committee should have realized that a New Millennium needs a major celebration – if not a lasting monument. "What about a Millennium Dome?" one of you will say. Good idea. But what are you going to put in it? Time for another committee meeting!

# JUNE

## Monday 14

## Tuesday 15

1215: King John signs Magna Carta.

## Wednesday 16

## Thursday 17

## Friday 18

## Saturday 19

## Sunday 20
### Father's Day

Whereas Mother's Day is a recognized festival, Father's Day is nothing of the sort. It came about by greeting card manufacturers thinking: "If we invented Father's Day we could sell more cards!"

# JUNE

## Monday 21

## Tuesday 22

Cancer starts here.

All star signs have their cross to bear, and Cancer is no exception. In their case it's a tendency to walk sideways, making it rather difficult for them to get anywhere fast. This naturally makes them rather snappy, so watch out for Cancerians – they can give you a nasty nip.

Cancer – the year ahead: Lots of going nowhere.

## Wednesday 23

**Thursday 24**
1876: Custer's last stand.

**Friday 25**

**Saturday 26**

**Sunday 27**

## Monday 28

Make this a tidy room week!

## Tuesday 29

## Wednesday 30

## Thursday 1 JULY

## Friday 2

## Saturday 3

## Sunday 4

Oh OK – try it next week instead!

### July – where does it come from?

The Romans originally called July Quintilis, which meant fifth month. When two extra months were added, they decided to rename it July, after Julius Caesar (Julie was the pet name they had for him). They did this partly because they were embarrassed about stabbing him to death in March.

## Monday 5

## Tuesday 6

Feast Day of Saint Sexburga. Yes, really!

## Wednesday 7

### Wednesday – what does it mean?

This is Woden's day. Woden was the Nordic one-eyed god of battle, though what use one eye is in battle I'm not sure. He carried a raven on each shoulder, which might explain what happened to his eye.

## Thursday 8

## Friday 9

## Saturday 10

Feast Day of Saint Hamburga. Not really, but it doesn't stop you having one.

## Sunday 11

## JULY

### Monday 12

Battle of the Boyne – bank holiday in N. Ireland (Orangemen's Day).

In this battle in 1690, King James II was defeated by William of Orange.

### Tuesday 13

### Wednesday 14

## Thursday 15

Saint Swithun's Day. Legend has it that if it rains on this day, it'll rain for 40 days. But doesn't it do that anyway at this time of year?

## Friday 16

## Saturday 17

## Sunday 18

THIS SHOULD STOP IT SOAKING THROUGH TO THE REST OF THE DIARY →

## JULY

### Monday 19

Planning a holiday? See if you can pick one where adults are illegal.

### Tuesday 20

### Wednesday 21

### Thursday 22

Leo starts here.

## Friday 23

Last day of term – isn't it?

## Saturday 24

## Sunday 25

The most fascinating thing about Leos is the way they eat in restaurants. They position themselves as far from their table as possible, and stand completely still. When their meal arrives they pounce on their food, causing gravy to fly in all directions. Be warned!

Leo – the year ahead: Being thrown out of even more restaurants than they have hot dinners.

# JULY

## Monday 26

## Tuesday 27

## Wednesday 28

1586: Sir Walter Raleigh first brought potatoes to England – by bike.

## Thursday 29

## Friday 30

## Saturday 31

## Sunday 1 AUGUST

**August – where does it come from?**
Just as July is named after Julius Caesar, so August is named after Augustus Caesar. It must be wonderful to be so famous that you get a month named after you. Actually my mother has got a day named after her – it's called Mother's Day. Come to think of it, so has my brother Pancake.

# HANDY HOLIDAY ADVICE

This time of year is usually when people go away on holiday. So here's a few handy holiday tips:

**Avoid family holidays**

They usually involve having your family with you! Obviously this one is a bit tricky – especially if your parents are paying!

**Take plenty of spending money**

If you have to rely on your parents for handouts, you'll have to stick with them for the whole holiday.

**Things to say to get rid of parents**

**Things NOT to say to get rid of parents**

Actually these two examples would probably work really well in the short term, but just wait till you get back home!

**Watch the food**

Obviously if you're going abroad you must sample the local delicacies, but avoid anything that's got anything live crawling about on it. This is probably not part of the dish, wherever you go.

**Watch the sun**

The last thing you want on holiday is to get sunburnt, or in this country rusty! So apply a sensible amount of sun block.

**Wear the right clothing**

HOLIDAY ROMANCES

Holidays, with their combination of sun, sea and sewer pipes, are the ideal time to have a romantic fling. But if you want it to be just that – a fling – there are a couple of ground rules:

**Don't use your real name**

This can be tricky if you've got a younger brother/sister who keeps calling you Philip or Carla when you've told your HH (Holiday Hotlips) that your name's Gary or Shauna.

**Don't tell them where you live**

After all, the last thing you want is them turning up on your doorstep. If the holiday romance develops into something more lasting, you can always tell them you've moved.

# AUGUST

## Monday 2

August bank holiday in Scotland.

## Tuesday 3

## Wednesday 4

## Thursday 5

## Friday 6

## Saturday 7

## Sunday 8

Peter Corey's birthday!

# AUGUST

## Monday 9

## Tuesday 10

## Wednesday 11

1897: Enid Blyton born.

## Thursday 12

The Glorious 12th – grouse season opens!

## Friday 13

Friday the 13th may be just a superstition, but fear of the number thirteen is a genuine medical condition, called triskaidekaphobia, and some people take it very seriously. For instance, there are no houses with the number 13 in France, in Italy they leave it out of the lottery and when Geneva's airport was built, there was no departure lounge 13 included, and on the 24 hour clock 1.00pm (1300 hours) was called 12a!

## Saturday 14

## Sunday 15

# AUGUST

## Monday 16

1977: Elvis Presley died – or did he?

## Tuesday 17

## Wednesday 18

## Thursday 19

## Friday 20

## Saturday 21

## Sunday 22

**Thursday – what does it mean?**

Thursday should really be Thor's day – the Norse god of thunder and melting snow. He was not a god to mess with, at least not without an umbrella handy. In Norse tradition Thursday was the sacred day, so why not become a modern-day Thor worshipper and get out of doing stuff on Thursdays?

# AUGUST

## Monday 23

Virgo starts here.

All Virgos will – at some point in their lives – own their own airline and multi-media megastore, go ballooning and have a silly-looking beard and an even sillier haircut. There's no escaping it, I'm afraid. Virgo – the year ahead: Lots and lots of having to put up with having more money than sense.

## Tuesday 24

## Wednesday 25

## Thursday 26

Take day off in name of Thor

## Friday 27

## Saturday 28

## Sunday 29

# HANDY BACK-TO-SCHOOL ADVICE

About now you'll be preparing to go back to school. You may be at the same school as last term, in which case there may be unfinished business to deal with:

Or you may be going to a new school, in which case there are loads of new situations to be confronted:

Either way, there's a number of things that need to be sorted.

## UNIFORM

If you've got to have a new one, make sure your parents pay for it (and not as a birthday present!) and make sure they get it in plenty of time for you to "customize" it.

## LUNCH BOX

Make sure this is now suitable for your school.

## TRANSPORT

Make sure this is also suitable for your school.

## HAPPY RETURN TO SCHOOL!

Even if there can NEVER be such a thing!

### Monday 30

Bank holiday in England, Wales and N. Ireland.

### Tuesday 31

### Wednesday 1 SEPTEMBER

Numa Pompilious now realized what a pig's ear he'd made of the new Roman calendar. Septem is Latin for seven, and September was now the ninth month. A committee was set up to consider a change of name: Tiberius, Germanicus and Tacitus were all suggested, after favourite emperors. One senator suggested "Puffa Puffa Rice" after his favourite breakfast cereal, but none of these caught on. So they stuck with September, and if anyone dared to say "But doesn't that mean seven?" they got to have lunch with the lions!

## Thursday 2

## Friday 3

Time to start developing some terrible disease that will prevent you having to go back to school

## Saturday 4

## Sunday 5

## Monday 6

Back to school about now – eugh!

## Tuesday 7

## Wednesday 8

## Thursday 9

## Friday 10

HANDY HINT –
TO AVOID JOINING
THE SCHOOL FOOTBALL
TEAM, BREAK YOUR
LEG!

## Saturday 11

Jewish New Year

## Sunday 12

# SEPTEMBER

## Monday 13

TO AVOID CROSS-COUNTRY RUNS. WHY NOT BREAK YOUR OTHER LEG?

## Tuesday 14

## Wednesday 15

## Thursday 16

## Friday 17

## Saturday 18

## Sunday 19

**Countdown to Millennium – update 3:**
By now you should have condensed your fascinating life into a number of items to exhibit in your Millennium Commemoration Theme Experience Thingy. You have probably got: a cycling proficiency badge, a dead pet, your first homework and a handful of strange photos. Your next task is to decide where to hold your Millennium Commemoration Theme Experience Thingy. Another committee meeting is needed!

## SEPTEMBER

### Monday 20

Today is Yom Kippur, the Jewish Day of Atonement.

### Tuesday 21

1866: HG Wells born.

### Wednesday 22

### Thursday 23

## Friday 24

Libra starts here.

Librans are constantly worried about weight. They're always picking things up in shops and weighing them in their hands, causing any heavily-disguised store detective to go on Red Alert. You may think this is odd, but hey – listen – it takes all sorts to make a world.

Libra – the year ahead: Lots of standing in shops with a handful of plums going "Hmmmm..."

## Saturday 25

## Sunday 26

Harvest Festival

## SEPTEMBER

### Monday 27

### Tuesday 28

### Wednesday 29

### Thursday 30

## Friday 1 OCTOBER

Yes! I know! October is the tenth month, even though octo means eight. By now the Romans had frankly given up trying to make sense of their calendar. If anyone sent them a rude letter pointing out how stupid it was they got invaded for their trouble.

## Saturday 2

## Sunday 3

# OCTOBER

## Monday 4

Feast day of Saint Francis of Assisi – friend to birds and animals.

## Tuesday 5

## Wednesday 6

## Thursday 7

## Friday 8

**Friday – what does it mean?**

Friday means the day of Frejya-Frigg, or Fridge-Freezer, great Goddess of the North, noted for her snowy white complexion, double doors (top and bottom), and little green light. A big woman, she had a huge cubic capacity, but it didn't matter where you put the soft scoop ice-cream, you could never serve it straight from her.

## Saturday 9

## Sunday 10

# OCTOBER

## Monday 11

## Tuesday 12

## Wednesday 13

Oh no! Wednesday the 13th! You'd better stay in bed all day in case something terrible happens to you – cos Wednesday the 13th is really dangerous, isn't it? Oh, no... that's FRIDAY the 13th! Oh well, stay in bed anyway – just to be on the safe side!

## Thursday 14

## Friday 15

## Saturday 16

## Sunday 17

**Countdown to Millennium – update 4:**
By now you and your committee are probably sitting surrounded by working models of your Millennium Dome built from drinking straws, paper plates and string. After staring at the models for some time, someone suggests using the garden shed. Now *that's* a good idea.

## OCTOBER

### Monday 18

### Tuesday 19

### Wednesday 20

### Thursday 21

## Friday 22

## Saturday 23

Scorpio starts here

If someone keeps accusing you of pinching their bottom, they're probably a Scorpio. They go through life as though they're being chased by a missile because they literally have a sting in their tail, which makes it extremely difficult for them to get their pants on.

Scorpio – the year ahead: Lots of saying "ouch!" for no apparent reason.

## Sunday 24

End of British Summer Time

# OCTOBER

## Monday 25

Half term – yeah! Or is it next week?

## Tuesday 26

## Wednesday 27

## Thursday 28

## Friday 29

## Saturday 30

## Sunday 31

Hallowe'en

# HALLOWE'EN - WHAT'S IT ALL ABOUT?

Hallowe'en, or All Hallows' Eve, is the last day of the Celtic calendar, and Druids believed that this was a time to honour the dead. They held a feast and invited the souls of all evil people, because they believed that when evil people died their souls were sentenced to live in the bodies of animals.

On that night, ghosts and demons wandered the earth, really putting the wind up innocent people! In those days it was called something like All Evil Night.

In AD 837 Pope Gregory IV changed the name to All Saints' Eve, because he didn't want ordinary people to think that ghosts were enjoying themselves. The word 'hallow' is Old English for 'saint'.

It was believed that ghosts and hobgoblins roamed the earth doing wicked things, but as they're invisible, children had to dress up and do it for them. That's where the idea for Trick or Treat came from.

Pumpkins are a symbol of harvest time, and the face on them (and the light inside them) are a tribute to the sun at harvest time.

HAPPY HALLOWE'EN!

# NOVEMBER

## Monday 1

## Tuesday 2

All Souls' Day. This is when dead members of your family are supposed to return and ask you difficult questions, like why you left a roller skate on the stairs.

## Wednesday 3

## Thursday 4

## Friday 5
Guy Fawkes' Day

Things NOT to do on Bonfire Night:
Put a lighted firework in your trousers.
Place your fireworks near the bonfire to keep them dry.
Sit your grandad near the bonfire when it's time to put the Guy on.

## Saturday 6

## Sunday 7
Hindu Festival of Diwali

## NOVEMBER

### Monday 8

1847: Bram Stoker – the creator of *Dracula* – was born.

Try to get an early night every night this week.

### Tuesday 9

10.30 – not bad!

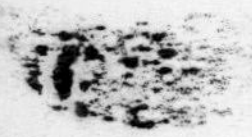

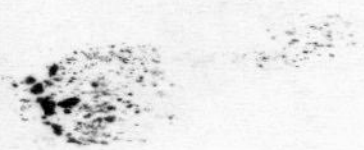

### Wednesday 10

10.00 - even better!

### Thursday 11

3.00 – is that A.M. or P.M?

## Friday 12

## Saturday 13

## Sunday 14

## NOVEMBER

### Monday 15

### Tuesday 16

### Wednesday 17

### Thursday 18

## Friday 19

## Saturday 20

## Sunday 21

**November – where does it come from?**
There was a half-hearted attempt to rename November Tiberius, but it never really took off. After all, there were feasts to prepare, chariots to race and Gauls to shout "What on earth are you talking about?" at. It wasn't easy conquering the known world, you know.

# NOVEMBER

## Monday 22

## Tuesday 23

Sagittarius starts here.

You'd think that being half-human, half-horse would be a difficult thing to live with, wouldn't you? But not for a Sagittarian. And why? Because of special trousers! Undetectable in everyday use, they are the one thing that prevents the Sagittarian from being ridiculed in public. (Special skirts are also available, as long as 28 days' notice is given.)

Sagittarius – the year ahead: Lots of refusing to enter knobbly knees competitions.

## Wednesday 24

## Thursday 25
Thanksgiving Day (USA)

## Friday 26

## Saturday 27

## Sunday 28

## Monday 29

## Tuesday 30

Saint Andrew's Day – patron saint of Scotland.

## Wednesday 1 DECEMBER

Despite being totally inaccurate the name December (10th month) remained, and even survived an attempt by the Emperor Commodus to rename it after his girlfriend. He wanted to call it *Amazonius*, because she was very tall. Her real name was Pauline, so I think we all had a narrow escape!

## Thursday 2

## Friday 3

## Saturday 4

The first day of the Jewish festival of Chanukkah.

## Sunday 5

# CHRISTMAS IS A TIME OF GIVING

. . . which is great. If only relatives realized that it is actually a time of giving something handy, not socks, ties, hand-knitted woollies with Winnie the Pooh on the front, etc. Of course, you will be under a certain amount of pressure to provide prezzies for them. Here are some tips:

**Aunties**: As you're only likely to see these people very rarely, get them something small, cheap and very breakable. Then put it in a box that's too big for it (with no padding), and wrap it in really interesting paper. The paper should cost much much more than the gift – at least £1. When you hand it to them they'll be so fascinated by the packaging that they'll put it up to their ear and shake it violently, saying: "Oooooh! What can it BE?!?" Having it so close to their ear they're certain to hear it break, and then won't have the heart to even unwrap it.

**Uncles**: Socks. If you don't give him socks he'll think there's something wrong with you and start making remarks like: "I told you that an expensive education would fill his head with fancy notions!" (or her head obviously if you're a girl and your uncle can tell the difference).

**Parents**: Anything that you really love, that you know they'll absolutely hate. Because then they are almost certain to let you have it once Christmas is over. If – in extreme circumstances – they say: "You don't mind if I exchange this at the shop, do you?" you can always say: "There's no need to do that! Here, I'll exchange it for this hand-knitted loo roll cosy that Auntie Mary gave me!"

**Grannies**: String. All grannies know that you can never own enough string.

**Grandads**: Toffees, especially if they haven't got their own teeth. That way you'll never go short of sweets over Christmas.

# DECEMBER

## Monday 6
Saint Nicholas' Day

Dear SANTA
Please Supply:
1. A sports car
2. A flame thrower
3. A new COMPUTER
4. £1,000,000,000

Start making your Christmas list!

## Tuesday 7

## Wednesday 8

## Thursday 9
The first day of Ramadhan.

## Friday 10

## Saturday 11

## Sunday 12

**Countdown to Millennium – update 5:**
Right – you've now established your Millennium Commemoration Theme Experience Thingy (a.k.a. garden shed), and arranged the display of your achievements. All that remains is to invite the public (a.k.a. mates) and cater for them – yes, it's time to get out the pop and Twiglets.

## DECEMBER

### Monday 13

Dear SANTA
Revised Xmas list:
1/ A new BIKE
2/ A computer GAME
3/ £1000

### Tuesday 14

### Wednesday 15

### Thursday 16

## Friday 17

## Saturday 18

Saturday is the day of *Saetere-Seater* or *Sevn-Seater*, the name given to the Sacred Celtic *Minne-Buss* – the winged and wheeled chariot that carried the seven gods of the week around their godly kingdom, except on Wednesdays when it was half-day closing. Of course, lots of people think Saturday is *Saturn's Day*, because they've never even heard of *Saetere-Seater*. Well, neither had I – until now.

## Sunday 19

# DECEMBER

## Monday 20

SANTA:
O.K. then, I'll
Settle for
1/ Some Socks
2/ A book
token

## Tuesday 21

## Wednesday 22

Capricorn starts here.

Never let a Capricorn do your laundry, because you'll never get it back. Why? Because they'll have eaten it! Yes! Every Zodiac sign has its little peculiarity, and Capricorn's is eating laundry.

Capricorn – the year ahead: Much spitting of buttons.

## Thursday 23

## Friday 24

Christmas Eve. Go to bed early without a fuss, or Santa won't come. It's true! Honest!

## Saturday 25

Christmas Day

## Sunday 26

This is normally Boxing Day – but because it's Sunday, it's been moved to Monday! Confused? Who cares! More chances to stuff your face!

Don't worry – the shops'll be open – so you can off-load those dodgy Xmas presents!

# DECEMBER

## Monday 27

Boxing Day – bank holiday England, Wales, Scotland and N. Ireland.

## Tuesday 28

ANOTHER bank holiday in England, Wales, Scotland and N. Ireland.

## Wednesday 29

Time to make those New Year's resolutions again

## Thursday 30

**Friday 31**

New Year's Eve, or Hogmanay. Party time!

**Saturday 1 JANUARY 2000**

New Year's Day

HAPPY NEW YEAR!
HAPPY NEW CENTURY!
HAPPY NEW MILLENNIUM!

Well, the New Millennium's here – but what will it hold? Once all the fuss and celebrations are out of the way, will it be very different? Or will it just be more of the same old stuff? Fortunately my book *Coping with the 21st Century* contains all the answers.

**Sunday 2**

New Year's holiday in Scotland.

Time to BREAK those New Year's resolutions again!

# So what's in the shed?

1 The Twiglet zone - A great big pile of Twiglets!
2 A full size model of the human body with explanatory labels. Oh all right, Gran.
3 Holiday zone - Relax on our virtual beach environment.
4 Future zone - Experience the technology of tomorrow (an old computer game and some Darth Vader bubble bath.)
5 The rusty bike-wheel and a can of old weed killer zone.
6 Geozone - learn about other countries from some of mum's holiday photo's and a couple of Geography books.
7 Zone of serious play. 8 Zone of stupid play.

THE MILLENNIUM SHED EXPERIENCE
1
HAIR
2
3
4
5
6
7
8
Shoulder
ARM
STRING
LEG
OTHER LEG
DIP DIP
Soup
IS THIS ONE OF THEM TRENDY CUT-AWAY ILLUSTRATIONS?
NAHH, THE SIDE OF THE SHED FELL OFF.

EMERGENCY PHONE NUMBERS

You just never know when you might need them!

**GENERAL EMERGENCIES**

POLICE ..................................................

FIRE .......................................................

AMBULANCE ..........................................

BREAKDOWN (TRANSPORT) ..................

BREAKDOWN (NERVOUS) .......................

GRANNY ...................................................

**PERSONAL EMERGENCIES**

HIT MAN ..................................................

MASTER FORGER ....................................

ALIBI PROVIDER ......................................

GRANNY ...................................................

As you can see I've put Granny twice – that's because Grannies are handy in ANY kind of emergency. Mainly because they're the one's with the string.

Scholastic Children's Books,
Commonwealth House, 1–19 New Oxford Street
London WC1A 1NU, UK

A division of Scholastic Ltd
London ~ New York ~ Toronto ~ Sydney ~ Auckland

First published by Scholastic Ltd, 1998



ISBN 0 590 11296 1

Typeset by TW Typesetting, Midsomer Norton, Somerset
Printed by Cox & Wyman Ltd, Reading, Berks.



10 9 8 7 6 5 4 3 2 1